Revision Notes for Standard Grade Biology

Tony Ablett
Tom Weston
Lesley Wood
(Trinity Academy, Edinburgh)

Published by
Chemcord
16 Inch Keith
East Kilbride
Glasgow

ISBN 1 870570 47 2

© Chemcord, 1992

First reprint, 1995
Second reprint. 1998

Printed by Bell and Bain Ltd, Glasgow

Note to students

The Course

This book is designed to cover all of the learning outcomes of the
Standard Grade Biology syllabus for examinations in 1994 onwards.

Exam structure

General paper $1^1/2$ hours   100 marks   approx. 50 KU : 50 PS

Credit paper $1^1/2$ hours   80 marks   approx. 40 KU : 40 PS

50% of the marks are awarded for knowledge and understanding (KU)
based only on the learning outcomes

50% of the marks are awarded for problem solving (PS)
The major PS activities are covered in the appendix

Symbols in the book

☐   general level material

▨   credit level material

Where general and credit level material occur together
in a table, the credit level material is outlined by a box

Using the book

You can indicate your knowledge of each statement with a ✔ in the
☐ at the left hand side

Space has been left at the right hand side so that you can make
additional notes

You can also mark statements with a highlighter pen

Exam advice

Make sure that you have a calculator, ruler, pen, pencil and rubber

Draw graphs lightly in pencil; when certain it's correct, go over in ink

Note whether a question is
                    KU - something you should know
                    PS - the answer lies in the information provided

Working through past papers is an essential part of your preparation

Your revision

● It is worth planning your revision in advance

● A **checklist of topics** has been provided below to allow you to keep track of your revision

● Use the **revision planner** on the next page to make up your own timetable for study

CHECKLIST OF TOPICS

REVISION PLANNER

Week	Topics	Check

THE BIOSPHERE

TOPIC 1   INVESTIGATING AN ECOSYSTEM

Definitions

☐

Term	Definition	Example
Habitat	the place where an organism lives	wood, mountain
Population	a group of organisms of one type	blue tits
Community	all organisms living in a habitat	animals + plants
Ecosystem	community + habitat	pond, soil

ABIOTIC FACTORS

☐

are non-living factors that affect an ecosystem   *e.g. temperature, moisture*

☐
▨

Abiotic factor	Method of measurement	Source of error	To reduce error
pH	pH paper or meter	contamination of sample	repeat readings and take an average
light intensity	light meter	shadow or cloud	

☐

Abiotic factors affect the distribution of organisms

e.g.

organism	abiotic factor	effect
fruit fly	light	move towards light
woodlouse	moisture	move from dry to moist

Organisms survive best in conditions that are most favourable

SAMPLING TECHNIQUES

Organism	Method of sampling	Source of error	To reduce error
plants	quadrat	non random sampling	random sampling
beetles	pitfall trap	too few samples	take many samples

THE BIOSPHERE

TOPIC 2   HOW IT WORKS

Definitions

☐

Term	Definition	Example
Producer	an organism that makes its own food	green plant
Consumer	an organism that eats other organisms	animal

Food chain

☐

| key ➤ direction of flow of energy |

producer ➤ consumer 1 ➤ consumer 2

e.g. oak leaf ➤ caterpillar ➤ blue-tit ➤ sparrow hawk

Food web

☐ A diagram showing the feeding relationships of animals and plants in an ecosystem

e.g. oak leaf ➤ caterpillar ➤ blue-tit ➤ sparrow hawk

greenfly ➤ ladybird

shrew

▨ Removing one species affects the numbers of remaining organisms in a food web e.g.

Organism removed	Organism affected	Effect	Reason
sparrow hawk	shrew	numbers rise	not eaten
sparrow hawk	caterpillar	numbers fall	more shrews so more eaten

Two ways that energy can be lost from a food web are

- heat
- waste

Type of pyramid	Definition	Diagram
numbers	shows relative numbers at each stage of food chain	consumer 2
biomass	shows relative mass at each stage of food chain	consumer 1 / producer

POPULATION GROWTH

growth rate = birth rate — death rate

if birth rate > death rate then population **increases**

if birth rate < death rate then population **decreases**

if birth rate = death rate then population is **stable**

Factors which can limit growth

supply of nutrients/water

predators

disease

space

Growth curve of a population under ideal conditions

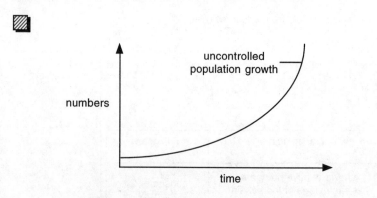

uncontrolled population growth occurs because
- birth rate increases
- death rate remains low due to absence of limiting factors

Competition

occurs when organisms have a need for the same resources
e.g.

Organism	Resources competed for	Effect
plants	light, moisture, nutrients	stronger species survive
animals	food, water, space	weaker species die

NUTRIENT CYCLES

nutrients   - *e.g. mineral salts, nitrogen*

         - are in limited supply

         - are locked in the bodies of organisms

         - must be released back into the ecosystem

The carbon and nitrogen cycles - see Topic 24

THE BIOSPHERE

TOPIC 3   CONTROL and MANAGEMENT

POLLUTION

☐   Contamination of the environment by substances that cause harm

☐

Main source of pollution	Example	Area affected	Control
Domestic	sewage	fresh water & sea	improved treatment
	CFCs from aerosols	air	use alternatives
	rubbish	land	recycling
Agricultural	fertiliser & pesticides	freshwater	organic farming
Industrial	sulphur dioxide	air	scrubbing

Energy sources and the environment

▨

Energy source	Adverse effect on environment
Nuclear power	radioactive waste is - harmful (causes cancers) - long lasting - difficult to dispose of
Fossil fuels	produce sulphur dioxide leading to acid rain
	produce carbon dioxide causing global warming

WATER POLLUTION

☐ Organic waste *e.g. human sewage* is a food source for microbes

Effect of microbes in polluted water

☐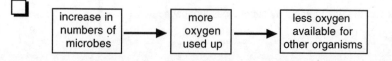

Effect of organic waste pollution in water

Low pollution		High pollution	Reason
low	**Numbers of microbes**	high	increased food supply for microbes
high	**Oxygen content**	low	microbes use up oxygen in aerobic respiration
many	**Numbers of species**	few	only a few species can tolerate low oxygen levels

INDICATOR SPECIES

is a species which, by its presence or absence, shows the level of a factor in the environment

e.g. lichens indicate the level of sulphur dioxide (SO_2) in air

SO_2 concentration	Lichen species present
low	*many leafy*
high	*few crusty*

MANAGEMENT OF NATURAL RESOURCES

☐

Natural resource	Poor management	Problems caused	Improvements
rainforest	destruction to provide land for crops	- loss of plant species - soil erosion - loss of fertility	increase productivity of existing farmland
fish in sea	overfishing	reduced stock	control of quotas

CONTROL OF AN ECOSYSTEM

▨ Agriculture and forestry aim to produce large quantities of a single crop by controlling the components of an ecosytem

Component	Control	Reason for control
soil minerals	fertiliser added	crop removed so no recycling of minerals
plants	herbicides	remove competitive species to ensure growth of crop
animals	pesticides	reduce pests to prevent crop being eaten

INVESTIGATING CELLS

TOPIC 4   INVESTIGATING LIVING CELLS

CELLS

☐   are the basic units of living things (**organisms**)

☐   Staining cells helps to show up structures more clearly
e.g. iodine for nuclei

☐   **Plant cell**   **Animal cell**

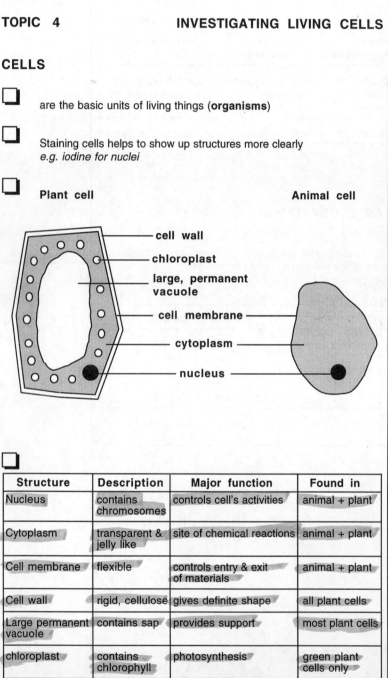

- cell wall
- chloroplast
- large, permanent vacuole
- cell membrane
- cytoplasm
- nucleus

☐

Structure	Description	Major function	Found in
Nucleus	contains chromosomes	controls cell's activities	animal + plant
Cytoplasm	transparent & jelly like	site of chemical reactions	animal + plant
Cell membrane	flexible	controls entry & exit of materials	animal + plant
Cell wall	rigid, cellulose	gives definite shape	all plant cells
Large permanent vacuole	contains sap	provides support	most plant cells
chloroplast	contains chlorophyll	photosynthesis	green plant cells only

INVESTIGATING CELLS

TOPIC 5   INVESTIGATING DIFFUSION

DIFFUSION

Definition

☐ The movement of substance(s) from high to low concentration of that substance

Importance to cell

☐ Allows entry/exit of O_2, dissolved food, CO_2 and water

Importance to organism

▨ Allows exchange of materials
e.g. between cells and blood in human

Model of diffusion

☐

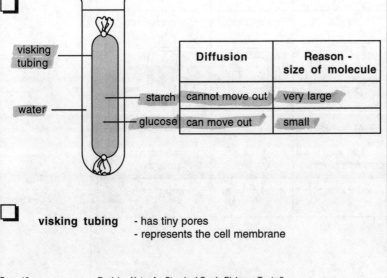

visking tubing

water

Diffusion	Reason - size of molecule
starch	cannot move out	very large
glucose	can move out	small

☐ **visking tubing**   - has tiny pores
- represents the cell membrane

OSMOSIS

☐ refers to the diffusion of water

Definition

▨

Movement of **water** through **a selectively permeable membrane** from **higher water concentration** (HWC) to **lower water concentration** (LWC) i.e. down the concentration gradient

Osmosis in cells

▨

Cell type	in pure water	in dilute solution	in concentrated solution
red blood cell	bursts	no change	shrinks
plant cell	turgid vacuole swells cell wall prevents bursting	no change	plasmolysed vacuole shrinks membrane pulls away
osmosis	water enters	water = water in out	water leaves

INVESTIGATING CELLS

TOPIC 6   INVESTIGATING CELL DIVISION

☐   Cell division is a means of increasing the number of cells in an
    organism and is controlled by the nucleus

☐   **Mitosis** is the division of the nucleus into two daughter nuclei which

▨   are identical to each other and to the original parent nucleus

Diagram	Description	Notes
	doubling of chromosomes	chromosomes long, thin, uncoiled and not clearly visible
	chromosomes shorten and thicken	centromere 2 identical chromatids
	chromosomes line up at the equator	centromeres attach to spindle fibres
	chromatids move to opposite poles	spindle fibres contract
	nuclei reform and cytoplasm divides	2 daughter cells with identical, full sets of chromosomes

▨   It is important that the full set of chromosomes (chromosome
    complement) is maintained so that no information is lost

INVESTIGATING CELLS

TOPIC 7   INVESTIGATING ENZYMES

Catalysts

☐
- speed up the rate of chemical reactions
- are unchanged at the end of a reaction

ENZYMES

☐
- are biological catalysts
- speed up the rate of chemical reactions in tissues
- are found in all living cells
- are proteins
- speed up **synthesis** & **breakdown** of substances
- are affected by **temperature** and **pH**
- are **specific** (act on only one type of substance due to their shape)

Enzyme reactions - breakdown

☐

Substrate	Enzyme	Product	Memory aid
hydrogen peroxide	catalase →	oxygen + water	hp cow
starch	amylase →	maltose	sam
fats	lipase →	fatty acids + glycerol	flag
protein	pepsin →	polypeptides	p^3

Enzyme reactions - synthesis

☐

Substrate	Enzyme	Product	Memory aid
glucose-1-phosphate	phosphorylase →	starch	g1pps

Effect of temperature

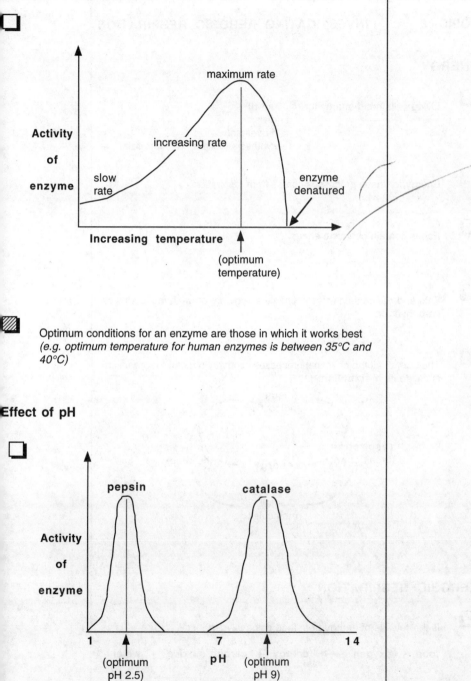

Optimum conditions for an enzyme are those in which it works best
*(e.g. optimum temperature for human enzymes is between 35°C and
40°C)*

Effect of pH

INVESTIGATING CELLS

TOPIC 8   INVESTIGATING AEROBIC RESPIRATION

ENERGY

☐   Living cells need energy for   - growth
- division
- movement
- synthesis (build up of chemicals)

☐   Energy for these processes comes from respiration

☐   Foods contain chemical energy

▨   Fats and oils contain more chemical energy per gram than proteins or carbohydrates

▨   The sum of all the chemical processes occuring in a cell (or organism) is called its **metabolism**

large
molecules

respiration   **synthesis**
(break down)   **energy**   (build up)

small
molecules

AEROBIC RESPIRATION

☐   is the release of energy from food using oxygen

food + oxygen ⟶ energy + carbon dioxide + water

Experiments that demonstrate aerobic respiration

Equation	Experiment	Result	Reason
FOOD	germinating seeds dried and weighed regularly	loss of dry weight	food used up
+			
OXYGEN	burning splint, gas jar, germinating seeds, damp cotton wool	burning splint goes out immediately	oxygen used up
↓			
ENERGY	thermometer, germinating seeds, vacuum flask	temperature rise	heat energy given out
+			
CARBON DIOXIDE	bicarbonate indicator or pH indicator or lime water, live animal	red → yellow / becomes more acidic / turns cloudy	carbon dioxide produced
+			
WATER	dry gas jar, burning food	condensation appears	water produced

The respirometer

Apparatus	Parts	Function	Result
	bubble of liquid	shows volume change	
	water bath	maintain constant temperature	bubble moves down due to oxygen uptake
	live animal	respiring	
	sodium hydroxide	absorbs CO_2	

CO_2 and living organisms

Colours	CO_2 level
purple	none
red	low
yellow	high

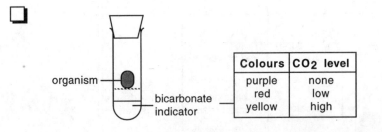

	animal in dark	animal in light	plant in dark	plant in dim light	plant in bright light
colour at start	red	red	red	red	red
colour at end	yellow	yellow	yellow	red	purple
CO_2 production	√	√	√	√	√
CO_2 uptake	x	x	x	√	√
processes occurring	respiration only			respiration and photosynthesis	

THE WORLD OF PLANTS

TOPIC 9

PLANT VARIETY

Advantages	Reason	Result of reduction in variety of plants
More types of habitat	can support greater variety of wild life	animals may become extinct
Different types of food	satisfy different dietary requirements	animals may become extinct
Source of medicines	can treat a range of diseases	loss of future medicines
Source of genes	breeding of better strains	not possible to introduce new genetic material

PLANT USES

	Example	Use
Raw materials	timber	construction paper
	cotton	clothing
Food	wheat	flour
	banana	staple food
Medicines	digitoxin (from foxgloves)	treatment of heart disease
	morphine (from poppies)	pain relief

PRODUCTION PROCESS

Timber *e.g. Norway Spruce*

Stage in production	Reason
Seeds in nursery	produce large numbers of healthy stock
Trenches prepared	drain soil
Young trees planted and protected	increase yield
Thinning	remove poorer trees
Harvesting after 50 years	trees have reached optimum size for profit making

POTENTIAL USES OF PLANTS

Potential Use	Notes
new medicines	plants may contain unknown substances that are effective against many diseases
new food sources	plants which can grow in very poor conditions may be valuable sources of food

THE WORLD OF PLANTS

TOPIC 10

SEEDS

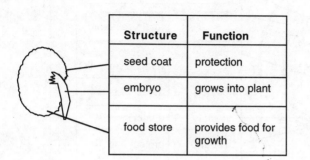

Structure	Function
seed coat	protection
embryo	grows into plant
food store	provides food for growth

GERMINATION

is the growth of a seed into a young plant

In order to germinate, seeds require **all** of the following

- water
- oxygen
- a suitable temperature

Effect of temperature on germination

Experimental set up
- equal numbers of the same type of seed
- same amount of water and air
- left for same time
- percentage germination calculated

Results

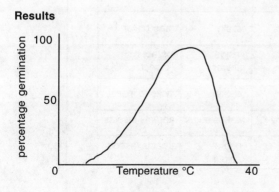

FLOWER STRUCTURE

Insect pollinated flower

Structure	Function
stigma	traps pollen
anther	produces pollen (male sex cells)
ovary	produces ovules (female sex cells)
petal	attract insects
nectary	attract insects
sepal	protect bud

WIND AND INSECT POLLINATED FLOWERS

Wind pollinated

Structure	Description	Reason
flower	dull no nectar	no need to attract insects
stigma	feathery	large surface to trap pollen
stamen	dangling	wind can spread pollen
pollen	light	spreads easily

Insect pollinated

Structure	Description	Reason
stigma	sticky	traps pollen
stamen	inside flower	contact with insect
pollen	sticky	sticks to insect
nectary	makes sugar	attracts insects
petal	bright colour	attracts insects

POLLINATION

☐

    is the transfer of pollen from anther to stigma

Types of pollination

☐

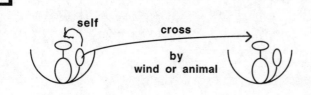

FERTILISATION

☐

    is the fusion of male and female sex cells

▨

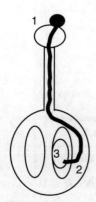

1 pollen grain grows tube

2 tube reaches ovule

3 gametes fuse and seed forms

FRUIT FORMATION

After fertilisation the ovary wall develops into the fruit

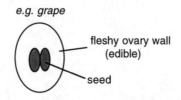

e.g. grape

fleshy ovary wall
(edible)

seed

SEED DISPERSAL

Spread of seeds away from parent plant to prevent overcrowding

Types of dispersal

Type	Example	Feature	Result
Wind	sycamore	winged	carried by wind
Animal internal	bramble	succulent colourful	eaten by animal seeds passed out in faeces
Animal external	burdock	hooked	sticks to coat falls off after a while

ASEXUAL REPRODUCTION

is the production of new plants from a single parent without
fertilisation

Types of asexual reproduction

Method	Example	Description
Runner	strawberry spider plant	parent runner offspring
Tuber	potato	swollen stem — shoot

A **clone** is the name given to the genetically identical plants
produced from a single parent plant

Advantages of sexual and asexual reproduction

 Sexual reproduction

Advantage	Reason
Variety of offspring	species has better chance of surviving a change in conditions
Wide distribution	less competition, spreads to new habitat

 Asexual reproduction

Advantage	Reason
Spreads over new area quickly	rapid growth
Offspring suited to environment	are identical to parent

ARTIFICIAL PROPAGATION

☐

Type	Description
Cuttings	take small part of plant and place in moist soil
Grafting	cut stem of one plant firmly fixed to rootstock of another plant

Advantages of artificial propagation

Allows production of plants on a commercial scale
- with desirable features
- in a short time
- in large numbers

THE WORLD OF PLANTS

TOPIC 11   **MAKING FOOD**

TRANSPORT SYSTEMS

☐

are needed to move
- raw materials to site of synthesis
- products to site where used or stored
- stored substances to growth areas

Transport tissues

☐ **Distribution in a young stem**

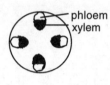

phloem
xylem

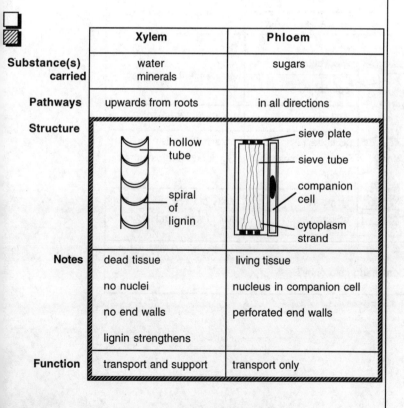

	Xylem	Phloem
Substance(s) carried	water minerals	sugars
Pathways	upwards from roots	in all directions
Structure	hollow tube / spiral of lignin	sieve plate / sieve tube / companion cell / cytoplasm strand
Notes	dead tissue / no nuclei / no end walls / lignin strengthens	living tissue / nucleus in companion cell / perforated end walls
Function	transport and support	transport only

LEAVES

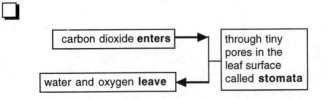

| carbon dioxide **enters** | → | through tiny pores in the leaf surface called **stomata** |
| water and oxygen **leave** | ← | |

Leaf structure

	Feature	Role in gas exchange
External	thin	rapid diffusion
	large surface area	
Internal	waxy cuticle	prevent leaf drying out
	epidermis	
	vein	brings water to leaf
	palisade ⎫	take in CO_2 give out
	⎬ mesophyll	O_2 during photosynthesis
	spongy ⎭	
	stoma in epidermis	entry of CO_2 exit of water and O_2

◯ = Containing chlorophyll

Experiments to show water loss from leaves

Set up	Result	Reason
oil - (prevents evaporation) water	water level falls	water loss through leaves
polythene bag (prevents evaporation)	weight goes down	water loss through leaves

Experiment to show stomatal distribution

Procedure   - **vaseline** blocks the stomata
                    - 4 leaves set up as below

Surfaces covered with vaseline	Water loss from	
both	neither	**Increasing**
lower	upper	**water**
upper	lower	**loss**
neither	both	↓

PHOTOSYNTHESIS

☐   is the process by which green plants make their own food

$$\text{carbon dioxide and water} \xrightarrow[\text{chlorophyll}]{\text{light}} \text{carbohydrate and oxygen}$$

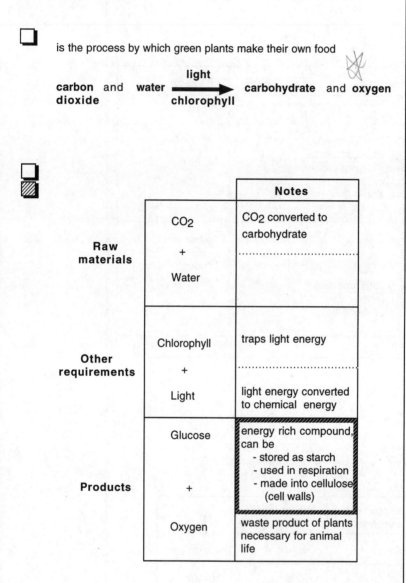

		Notes
Raw materials	CO_2 + Water	CO_2 converted to carbohydrate ....
Other requirements	Chlorophyll + Light	traps light energy .... light energy converted to chemical energy
Products	Glucose + Oxygen	energy rich compound, can be - stored as starch - used in respiration - made into cellulose (cell walls)
		waste product of plants necessary for animal life

☐   The presence of **starch** shows that photosynthesis has taken place

Testing a Leaf for Starch

Step	Reason
1 boil in water	soften and kill leaf
2 boil in alcohol	remove chlorophyll
3 rinse in water	soften leaf
4 add iodine	turn starch black

Experiments to show requirements for photosynthesis

Steps common to all experiments

Step	Reason
1 leave in dark for 24 hours	destarch plant
2 variable factor tested	experiments (see over)
3 leave for time	so plant can make starch
4 test for starch	show if photosynthesis has taken place

	Experiment	Result of starch test	Reason
Light	card blocks light	black brown	light → starch made .... no light → no starch made
Carbon dioxide	sodium hydroxide removes CO_2 CO_2 present	brown black	no CO_2 → no starch made .... CO_2 → starch made
Chlorophyll	white (no chlorophyll) green (chlorophyll) variegated leaf	brown black	no no chlorophyll → starch made .... chlorophyll → starch made

Measuring the rate of photosynthesis

Elodea bubbler

	Set up	Reason
	test tube	gas can be collected
	sodium bicarbonate solution	source of carbon dioxide
	gas bubbles	counting number of bubbles released in set time gives measure of rate of photosynthesis
	Elodea	photosynthesising plant

LIMITING FACTORS

A limiting factor slows down photosynthesis when in short supply

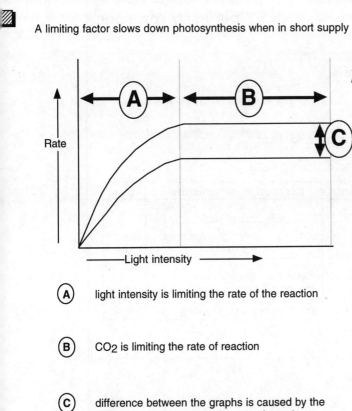

(A) light intensity is limiting the rate of the reaction

(B) CO_2 is limiting the rate of reaction

(C) difference between the graphs is caused by the effect of temperature on the rate of reaction

ANIMAL SURVIVAL

TOPIC 12 THE NEED FOR FOOD

☐ Animals need food for

- energy *e.g. movement , heat*
- raw materials for growth and repair

Carbohydrates, Proteins and Fats

▨

	Elements	Description of structure	Use
Carbohydrate	C , H , O	simple - one or two sugar units *e.g. glucose* ·· complex - many glucose units *e.g. starch*	e n e r g y
Fat	C , H , O	fatty acids + glycerol	
Protein	C , H , O , N	amino acids joined together	growth repair

DIGESTION

☐

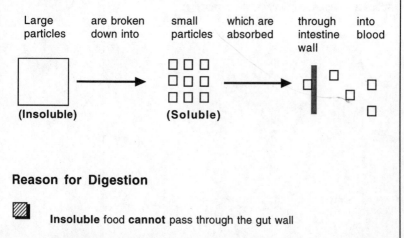

Large particles	are broken down into	small particles	which are absorbed	through intestine wall	into blood

(Insoluble)   **(Soluble)**

Reason for Digestion

▨

Insoluble food **cannot** pass through the gut wall

Soluble food **can** pass through the gut wall

CARNIVORE

incisor
canine
carnassial teeth

	Carnivore *e.g. dog*		Herbivore *e.g. sheep*	Omnivore *e.g. human*
Incisor	biting		biting	biting
Canine	killing		biting	biting
Premolar + Molar	shearing + slicing crushing	carnassials	grinding	crushing

horny pad
incisor
canine
space

HERBIVORE

MAMMALIAN ALIMENTARY CANAL *e.g. human*

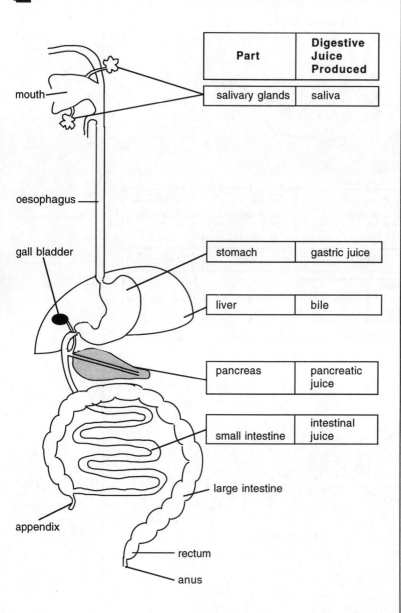

Part	Digestive Juice Produced
salivary glands	saliva
stomach	gastric juice
liver	bile
pancreas	pancreatic juice
small intestine	intestinal juice

mouth

oesophagus

gall bladder

large intestine

appendix

rectum

anus

Bile

Bile is
- produced in the liver
- stored in the gall bladder
- contains no digestive enzymes

Peristalsis

is the movement of food through the gut

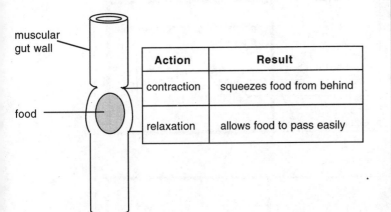

muscular gut wall

food

Action	Result
contraction	squeezes food from behind
relaxation	allows food to pass easily

DIGESTION AND ABSORPTION OF FOOD

Part	Description
mouth	mixes food with saliva containing salivary amylase

stomach	protein digesting enzyme produced	contractions mix food with pepsin and hydrochloric acid (helps breakdown)

small intestine
(digestion part)

pancreatic juice contains the enzymes

carbohydrates ———— amylase
fats ———— lipase
protein ———— protease
broken down by different enzymes

See Topic 7

small intestine
(absorption part)

Feature	Reason
good transport system	carries away products of digestion
moist thin walls large surface	increased efficiency of diffusion

villus

blood carries away glucose and amino acids

lacteal carries away glycerol and fatty acids

large intestine	water absorbed faeces stored in rectum, eliminated through anus

ANIMAL SURVIVAL

SEX CELLS

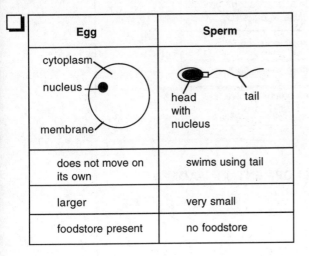

Egg	Sperm
cytoplasm, nucleus, membrane	head with nucleus, tail
does not move on its own	swims using tail
larger	very small
foodstore present	no foodstore

FERTILISATION

is the fusing together of a sperm nucleus and an egg nucleus to form a single cell called a zygote

Types of fertilisation

Type	Description	Organism
External	fertilisation outside the female's body	fish
Internal	fertilisation inside the female's body	mammals

Internal fertilisation is important to land living animals because it prevents the sex cells being exposed to air and so drying out

REPRODUCTION AND DEVELOPMENT IN FISH

☐

e.g. salmon, trout, stickleback

Fertilisation	in a 'nest', sperm brought close to eggs
Protection of eggs	flexible covering
Embryo food supply	from yolk in egg
Young fish	on hatching have no parental care

REPRODUCTION AND DEVELOPMENT IN MAMMALS
e.g. human

Production of sex cells

☐

Sex cells	Where produced
sperm	testes
eggs	ovaries

Fertilisation

☐

ovary	releases egg into oviduct
oviduct	where **fertilisation** takes place
uterus	where egg implants

Movement of egg down oviduct

☐

     is brought about by
- sweeping of tiny hairs
- muscular movements of oviduct

Implantation

☐

     Developing egg attaches to uterus wall

Development

☐

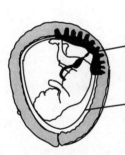

Structure	Function
placenta	where embryo obtains food from mother's blood
amniotic sac	filled with fluid to protect embryo

Placenta

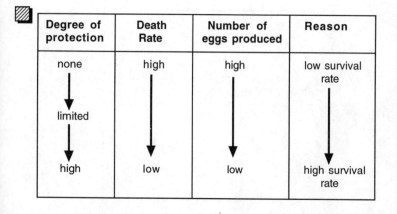

mother's
blood
supply

Description	Function	
highly folded	allows exchange of materials from	
blood supplies separate but brought close together	**mother to embryo** oxygen food	**embryo to mother** waste carbon dioxide

embryo
blood
supply

PARENTAL CARE IN MAMMALS

At birth young mammals are dependent on the adult for care and protection

Care and protection of young

Degree of protection	Death Rate	Number of eggs produced	Reason
none ↓ limited ↓ high	high ↓ low	high ↓ low	low survival rate ↓ high survival rate

ANIMAL SURVIVAL

TOPIC 14   WATER AND WASTE

WATER BALANCE

☐

Water gain	Water loss
food and drink respiration	sweat from skin breath from lungs urine faeces

KIDNEYS

☐ are the main organs for regulating water content in a mammal

☐

Structure	Function
renal artery	bring blood to kidney
renal vein	carry blood away from kidney
kidney	regulates water removes waste
ureter	carries urine to bladder
bladder	stores urine

Kidney Functions

☐
- filters blood (separates large and small molecules)
- reabsorbs useful materials *e.g. glucose*

Urea

☐
Urea is

- a waste product
- removed in urine

▨
- produced in the liver from the breakdown of amino acids
- transported to the kidneys in the blood

Nephron structure

▨

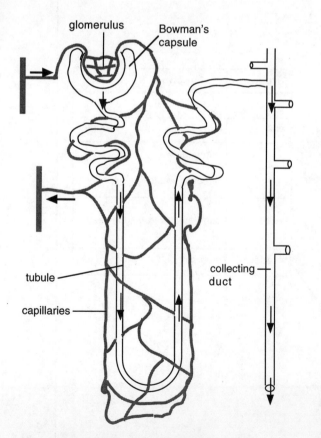

glomerulus

Bowman's capsule

tubule

capillaries

collecting duct

Structure	Function	Description
glomerulus	blood filtration	protein stays in blood water glucose forced out of blood urea
Bowman's capsule	collects filtrate	contains water glucose urea
tubule capillaries	reabsorption	useful materials leave tubule and re-enter blood *e.g. glucose, water*
collecting duct	gathers urine from several nephrons	contains urea water

DH and Water balance

Anti diuretic hormone

- regulates water balance
- is produced in the pituitary gland
- acts on the kidney

Blood water concentration	ADH production	Effect	Urine output
low	increases	more water reabsorbed into blood	little and concentrated
high	decreases	less water reabsorbed into blood	lots and dilute

Kidney Damage

Cause	Implications
accident or disease	kidney failure toxic waste builds up in body death will occur unless waste removed

Treatment of kidney failure

Method	Benefits	Limitations
kidney transplant	lead relatively normal life	lack of donors possibility of tissue rejection
kidney machine	keeps patient alive until suitable donor found no rejection	long periods of time spent on dialysis

ENVIRONMENTAL FACTORS AFFECTING BEHAVIOUR

Factor	Organism	Response to change	Significance of behaviour	
Light	maggot	moves away from bright light	increases chance of finding food, moisture and shelter	increases

chance |
| Chemicals | planaria | moves towards chemicals from food | increases chance of finding food | of |
| Humidity | woodlouse | increase move-ment in dry, decrease in moist/damp | will move out unfavourable remain in favourable | survival |

Experiment to show factors affecting behaviour

Choice chamber

hole for introducing organisms

shaded side ⌐_____ light side

Step	Reason
1 **10** woodlice put in chamber	accounts for variation in behaviour
2 left for 10 minutes	allows time for response
3 distribution noted	record result
Result more woodlice found in shaded side	have remained in favourable conditions and moved out of unfavourable conditions

RHYTHMICAL BEHAVIOUR

Example	Trigger	Organism	Description of behaviour	Significance
Tidal	movement of tide	limpet	remains attached to rocks at low tide, moves freely at high tide	prevents drying allows feeding
Daily (circadian)	light/dark	owl	sleeps during day, active at night	prey active at night
Annual	daylength	swallow	migrate north in summer, south in winter	moves to area where food supply and temperature are suitable
	daylength	brown bear	hibernates in winter	conserves energy when food supply is low

HE HUMAN SKELETON

☐ has three functions
- support
- muscle attachment
- protection of heart, lungs, brain and spinal cord

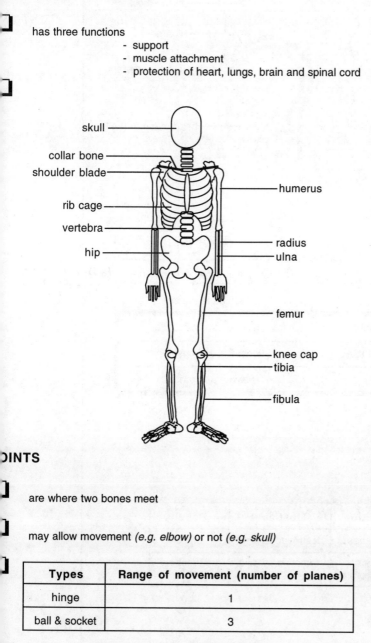

OINTS

☐ are where two bones meet

☐ may allow movement *(e.g. elbow)* or not *(e.g. skull)*

Types	Range of movement (number of planes)
hinge	1
ball & socket	3

Synovial joint

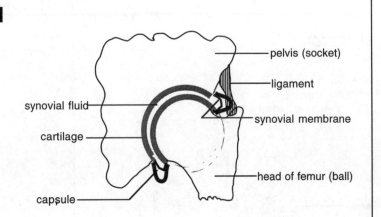

pelvis (socket)

ligament

synovial fluid

synovial membrane

cartilage

head of femur (ball)

capsule

Structure	Function
cartilage	cushions and protects bone ends *Acts as shock absorber*
ligament	holds bones together
synovial membrane	secretes synovial fluid
synovial fluid	lubricates and cushions
capsule	encases and protects

BONE

Composition	Treatment	Result
flexible fibres	destroyed by heat	brittle
hard minerals (calcium phosphate)	removed by acid	soft/rubbery

Bone is formed by living cells

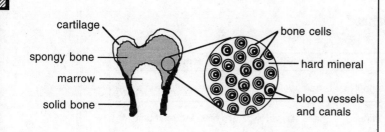

MUSCLES

can either contract or relax

can only exert a force when they contract

Contract	Relax
actively shorten	passively lengthen
cause movement	cause no movement

must be arranged as an opposing (**antagonistic**) pair at a joint to cause both bending and straightening *e.g. arm*

	Biceps	Triceps
Bending	contracts	relaxes
Straightening	relaxes	contracts

are attached to bone by **tendons**

Tendons are inelastic

reason - so that the force produced by a muscle is transferred to the bone

THE BODY IN ACTION

Energy imbalance

☐

Energy	Result	Reason
input > output	gain weight	extra energy stored as fat
input < output	lose weight	stored fat used up

Effects of breathing on gases

☐

Gas	Inhaled air (into lungs)	Exhaled air (out of lungs)	Absorbed / Released
O_2	20 %	16 %	absorbed
CO_2	0.03 %	4 %	released

The Internal Structure of the Lungs

☐

Structure	Description
trachea	air passages from
bronchus	the mouth to the
bronchiole	alveolus
alveolus	tiny, thin walled air sac

Detailed structure of the trachea

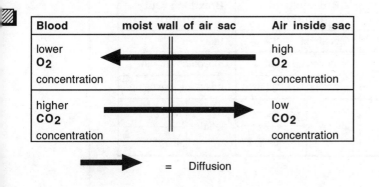

Structure	Description	Function
cartilage	incomplete rings	keeps trachea open
mucus	sticky fluid	traps dirt and germs
cilia	tiny hairs	moves mucus up out of air passages to be swallowed

O——► inner trachea wall magnified

Gas exchange in the alveolus

Blood	moist wall of air sac	Air inside sac
lower O_2 concentration	◄————	high O_2 concentration
higher CO_2 concentration	————►	low CO_2 concentration

————► = Diffusion

Features of the lung making gas exchange efficient

Feature	Reason
good blood supply	rapid transport of gases
alveolar surface is - moist - thin - large s.a.	increased efficiency of diffusion

Breathing mechanism - structures involved

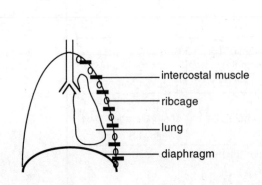

- intercostal muscle
- ribcage
- lung
- diaphragm

Structures	Breathing In (Inhale)	Breathing Out (Exhale)
intercostals	contract	relax
ribcage	moves up + out	moves down + in
diaphragm	contracts + flattens	relaxes + moves up
lungs	inflate — vol ↑ / pressure ↓	deflate — vol ↓ / pressure ↑

THE HEART

Chambers and valves

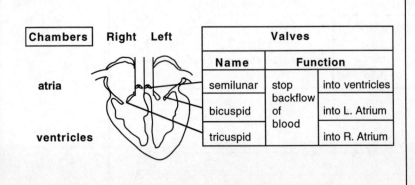

Chambers	Right	Left
atria		
ventricles		

Valves		
Name	Function	
semilunar	stop backflow of blood	into ventricles
bicuspid		into L. Atrium
tricuspid		into R. Atrium

Bloodflow through the heart

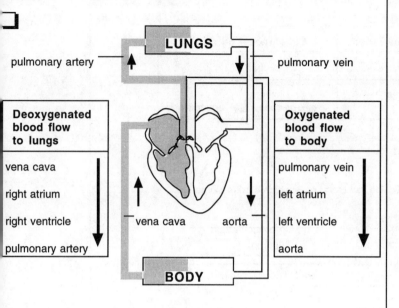

The muscular wall of the left ventricle is thicker than the right ventricle because the left ventricle pumps the blood **further**

The heart obtains its blood supply from the coronary arteries

BLOOD

Vessels

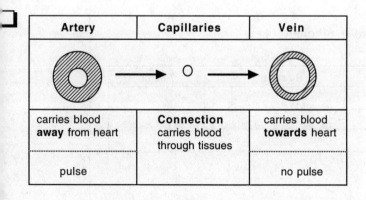

Artery	Capillaries	Vein
carries blood **away** from heart	**Connection** carries blood through tissues	carries blood **towards** heart
pulse		no pulse

Transport

Part of the blood	Substances carried
red blood cells	oxygen
plasma	others *e.g. glucose, CO_2, amino acids*

Haemoglobin

The chemical in red blood cells which carries oxygen

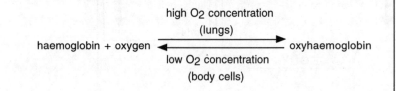

$$\text{haemoglobin} + \text{oxygen} \xrightleftharpoons[\substack{\text{low } O_2 \text{ concentration} \\ \text{(body cells)}}]{\substack{\text{high } O_2 \text{ concentration} \\ \text{(lungs)}}} \text{oxyhaemoglobin}$$

CAPILLARY NETWORK

Movement of gases

	Body cell	Capillary	
O_2	in	out	gases move by diffusion
CO_2	out	in	

Features that make it efficient

Feature	Reason	Result
thin walled	easier to pass through	
dense network	all cells close to capillary	rapid diffusion
large surface area	more exchange possible	

THE EYE

Structure and function

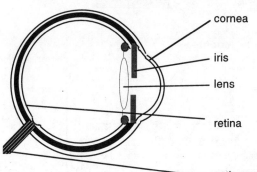

Structure	Major function
cornea	let light in
iris	control amount of light entering
lens	focus light onto retina
retina	change light into nerve messages
optic nerve	carries messages to the brain

Judgement of distance

No of Eyes	Judgement of distance	Information to brain	Result
two	accurate	2 different images	3D picture
one	inaccurate	1 image	no 3D picture

THE EAR

Structure and function

☐

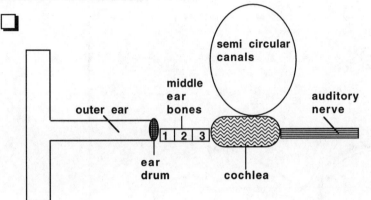

Structure	Major Function
ear drum	passes vibrations to ear bones
middle ear bones	amplify and transmit vibrations
cochlea	changes vibrations to nerve messages
auditory nerve	carries messages to brain

Semi circular canals

☐ sense head movements and position. Important in balance

▨ Three canals at right angles sense movement of the head in all three planes

Direction of sound

☐ can be more accurately judged with two ears rather than one

THE NERVOUS SYSTEM

is composed of the brain, spinal cord and nerves

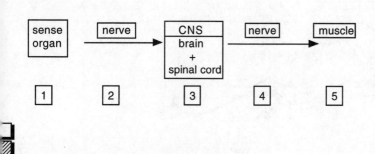

Structure	Function
1	receive information change to nerve message
2	carry message to CNS
3	process information send out messages
4	carry message to muscle
5	response

The Brain

Structure	Function
cerebrum	- interprets messages from sense organs - sends messages to muscles - memory, reason, intelligence
cerebellum	muscular control and balance
medulla	- automatic actions - rate of breathing, heartbeat

Reflex Action

A rapid, automatic response protecting the body from damage

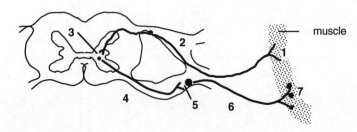

Pathway	Number	Part	Description
	1	receptor	receives stimulus and changes it to a nerve impulse
	2	sensory neurone	carries impulse to CNS
	3	synapse	tiny gap, junction of nerves
	4	connector neurone	carries impulse directly from sensory to motor neurone
	5	synapse	tiny gap, junction of nerves
	6	motor neurone	carries impulse to muscle
	7	nerve ending in muscle	causes contraction (response)

Transmission through a synapse

sensory nerve → **synapse** → **connector nerve**

electrical impulse | chemical | electrical impulse

TOPIC 19   CHANGING LEVELS OF PERFORMANCE

Muscle fatigue

Condition	Circumstance	Cause	Due to
muscle fatigue	strenuous exercise	lack of O_2	supply not meeting demand
		lactic acid	increased anaerobic respiration

Effect of exercise

Muscles demand more energy and therefore carry out respiration faster

	Reason	Resultant increase in
Pulse rate Increases	to increase blood flow through muscles	O_2 supply food supply CO_2 removal
Breathing rate Increases	to Increase gas exchange	O_2 uptake CO_2 removal

	Trained athlete	Untrained person	Reason
Breathing rate Lactic acid level	increases	greater increase	training improves efficiency of lungs and circulation
Recovery Time (to return to normal levels)	short	long	oxygen reaches muscles more quickly

INHERITANCE

VARIATION

SPECIES

☐ A **species** is a group of interbreeding organisms whose offspring are fertile

☐ Members of a species are different from each other - they show **variation**

VARIATION

▨	Continuous variation	Discontinuous variation
Examples	height weight seed mass leaf size	ear lobes eye colour flower colour tongue rolling
Definition	show a gradual range from one extreme to another	show distinct differences
Shown by	*e.g. height* **histogram** nos ↑ small ⟶ big	*e.g. ear lobes* **bar chart** nos ↑ present ⟶ absent

WHAT IS INHERITANCE?

INHERITED CHARACTERISTICS

❏ Certain characteristics are determined by genetic information inherited from both parents

❏ The **phenotype** is the appearance of an organism resulting from inherited characteristics

Examples of inherited characteristics

❏

Characteristic	Possible phenotypes
coat colour in mice	black, brown
eye colour in fruit flies	red, white
height in pea plants	tall, dwarf

❏ These inherited characteristics are carried on **chromosomes**

CHROMOSOME SETS

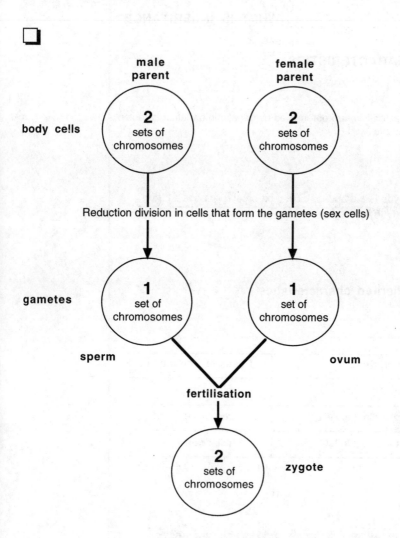

Revision Notes for Standard Grade Biology - Topic 21

Term	Definition
Gene	part of a chromosome controlling **one** characteristic
Alleles	different forms of a gene that control a characteristic
Dominant	allele that always shows itself in the phenotype
Recessive	allele that is masked by a dominant one
True breeding	an organism that has either 2 dominant or 2 recessive alleles
Genotype	genetic make up (always written in letters)
Phenotype	appearance (always written in words)

MONOHYBRID CROSSES

involve breeding between individuals different for **one** characteristic

True breeding cross

Gene	Alleles	Relationship	Symbols
coat colour in mice	black	dominant	B
	brown	recessive	b

P (parents)	phenotype	black male x brown female
	genotype	BB x bb
parental gametes	genotype	all B x all b
F1 (first generation)	genotype	all Bb
	phenotype	all black
F1 selfed (crossed together)	genotype	Bb x Bb
F1 gametes	genotype	half B half B x half b half b
random fertilisation (shown in a Punnett square)		<table><tr><td>sperm eggs</td><td>B</td><td>b</td></tr><tr><td>B</td><td>BB</td><td>Bb</td></tr><tr><td>b</td><td>Bb</td><td>bb</td></tr></table>
F2 (second generation)	genotypes	BB : 2Bb : bb
	phenotypes	3 black : 1 brown exact 3:1 ratios rarely occur because of random fertilisation

Monohybrid crosses continued

Backcross

 Recessive phenotypes have a known genotype
e.g. a brown mouse must be bb

 Dominant phenotypes have unknown genotypes
e.g. a black mouse is either BB or Bb

 A **backcross** determines unknown genotype

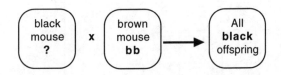

Then **black** mouse must be **BB**

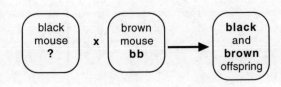

Then **black** mouse must be **Bb**

SEX DETERMINATION

☐

Humans have 46 chromosomes - 44 + 2 sex chromosomes

Male	Female
44	44
+	+
XY	XX

Inheritance of sex chromosomes

☐

Parents	male	female
	XY	XX
Gametes	X or Y sperm	X ova
Fertilisation	♂ / ♀	X	Y
	X	XX	XY
Offspring	1 female : 1 male	

INHERITANCE

SELECTIVE BREEDING

❑

    is choosing parents with desired characteristics to improve stocks

❑

Organism	Improved characteristic
cattle	growth - beef production
	yield - milk production
potato	disease resistance - to fungus

Mechanism of selective breeding

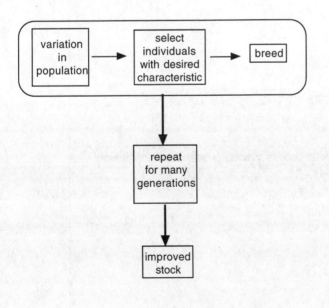

```
┌──────────────────────────────────────────────────────┐
│  variation      select                                 │
│  in          →  individuals    →  breed                │
│  population     with desired                            │
│                 characteristic                          │
└──────────────────────────────────────────────────────┘
                        │
                        ▼
                    repeat
                    for many
                    generations
                        │
                        ▼
                    improved
                    stock
```

CHROMOSOME MUTATIONS

❏
   A mutation is a change in structure or number of chromosomes

Effect of mutations

	Organism	Mutation	Result
Harmful	human	extra chromosome	Down's syndrome
Useful	wheat	extra sets of chromosomes	increased yield

Factors increasing rate of mutation

- **radiation** e.g. UV light, X-rays, atomic
- **chemicals** e.g. mustard gas

Amniocentesis

❏
   is the sampling of amniotic fluid containing foetal cells

❏
   is used for the detection of chromosome abnormalities before birth

BIOTECHNOLOGY

TOPIC 23   LIVING FACTORIES

❑ **Biotechnology** is the use of microbes and raw materials to produce useful substances

YEAST

❑ is used in   - **baking** to raise dough
                 - **brewing** to produce alcohol

❑ is a single celled fungus

❑ cannot photosynthesise, but uses sugar as a food source

FERMENTATION

❑ Process carried out by yeast **in the absence of oxygen**

❑
$$sugar \xrightarrow[\text{(yeast)}]{\text{fermentation}} alcohol + carbon\ dioxide + energy$$

▨ Fermentation is also called **anaerobic respiration**

A comparison of the two types of respiration in yeast

▨

	Aerobic	Anaerobic
Oxygen required	always	never
Amount of energy released	more	less
End products	carbon dioxide + water	carbon dioxide + alcohol

BREWING

Important processes

Process	Description	Reason	
malting	germination of barley to convert starch into sugar	yeast unable to digest starch needs sugar as a food supply	
fermentation	vessels + nutrients sterilised	prevents growth of other microbes	optimum conditions
	malt dissolved	provides sugar as a food supply	for growth of
	thermostatic control	provides constant temperature	yeast

Batch processing

Fermentation of one lot is completed before the next can begin
e.g. brewing

MILK

☐

Bacteria are needed to make **cheese** and **yoghurt** from milk

Souring of milk

☐

Souring of milk is a fermentation process

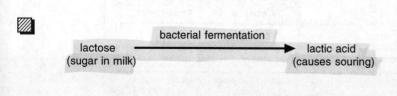

lactose
(sugar in milk) → bacterial fermentation → lactic acid
(causes souring)

BIOTECHNOLOGY

TOPIC 24   PROBLEMS AND PROFIT WITH WASTE

SEWAGE

❑   is organic waste from humans

Untreated sewage

❑   causes pollution of water supplies

Result	Effect
bacteria release minerals	waterweeds grow rapidly and clog waterway
bacteria use up oxygen	reduced numbers of animal species

❑   causes diseases
- dysentery
- typhoid
- cholera

Treatment of sewage

❑   **Main process**

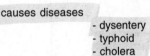

| sewage | → decay microbes → | products harmless to environment |

▨   Oxygen is added to create aerobic conditions so that bacteria
- grow faster
- are more efficient
- break down sewage completely

❑   Oxygen is provided by
- compressed air forced through sewage
- sewage sprayed onto stone beds

▨   One species of microbe cannot break down all the different
substances in sewage, so many different species are needed

WASTE

Upgrading waste using microbes

☐

▨

Waste	Useful product	Economic importance	Advantages
manure	methane gas	prevents pollution from waste	fuel source
methanol	protein	saves cost of disposal	food source

FUELS

☐ Alcohol and methane are produced by fermentation

☐ Fuel obtained from fermentation has advantages over fossil fuel in that it is in unlimited supply

MICROBES

☐ When conditions are suitable (*e.g. good food supply, suitable temperature*) microbes reproduce rapidly by asexual means

☐ Microbes can be grown and harvested to produce foods rich in protein

DECAY

is the breakdown of dead organisms and waste by microbes

allows the recycling of nutrients (*e.g. carbon and nitrogen*)

Dead organisms provide a source of energy for microbes

THE CARBON CYCLE

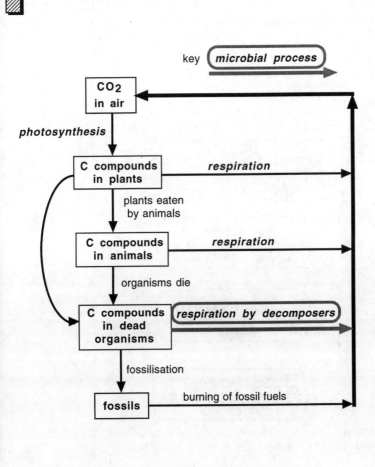

THE NITROGEN CYCLE

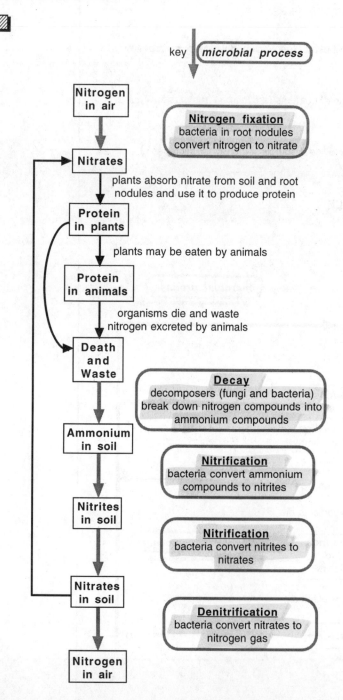

key — *microbial process*

Nitrogen in air

Nitrogen fixation
bacteria in root nodules convert nitrogen to nitrate

Nitrates

plants absorb nitrate from soil and root nodules and use it to produce protein

Protein in plants

plants may be eaten by animals

Protein in animals

organisms die and waste nitrogen excreted by animals

Death and Waste

Decay
decomposers (fungi and bacteria) break down nitrogen compounds into ammonium compounds

Ammonium in soil

Nitrification
bacteria convert ammonium compounds to nitrites

Nitrites in soil

Nitrification
bacteria convert nitrites to nitrates

Nitrates in soil

Denitrification
bacteria convert nitrates to nitrogen gas

Nitrogen in air

SAFE HANDLING OF MICROBES

❑ Microbes must be handled with great care to avoid **contamination**

❑ Contamination is

- the introduction of unwanted microbes into cultures
- the spread of microbes that cause disease

Precaution	Reason
use of disinfectant	to kill unwanted microbes
use of heat	
laboratory coats worn	to avoid contamination
hands washed/gloves worn	
cultures sealed	

RESISTANT SPORES

❑ are produced by microbes in certain conditions

Conditions	e.g.	Microbial activity
favourable	20-40°C	multiply and grow no spores produced
unfavourable	100°C	no growth, but form resistant spores

❑ Manufacturing processes must kill spores or prevent their entry in order to avoid contamination

e.g. sterilisation at 125°C

BIOTECHNOLOGY

TOPIC 25   REPROGRAMMING MICROBES

GENETIC ENGINEERING

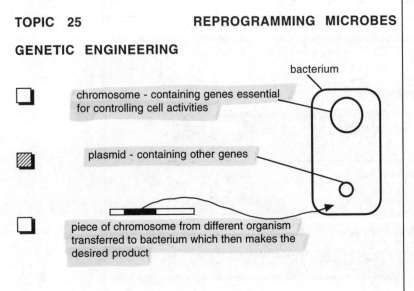

bacterium

☐ chromosome - containing genes essential for controlling cell activities

▨ plasmid - containing other genes

☐ piece of chromosome from different organism transferred to bacterium which then makes the desired product

☐ e.g.

Product	Application
insulin	treatment of diabetes
growth hormone	treatment of hormone deficiency

Diagram	Step
	required gene identified and cut out
	bacterial plasmid cut open
	gene inserted into plasmid
	plasmid + gene inserted into bacterium
	bacteria grown in favourable conditions
	product extracted and purified

Genetic engineering allows greater quantities of product to be obtained in a shorter time

More insulin produced by biotechnology is needed because

- there are more diabetics
- diabetics live longer
- more people are allergic to insulin obtained from animal sources

New genotypes can be produced by either genetic engineering or selective breeding

	Genetic engineering	Selective breeding
Number of generations required for change	one	many
Time taken to produce improved variety	quick	slow
Chance that desired change will occur	very good	poor
Quality and quantity of product	excellent	variable

BIOLOGICAL DETERGENTS

contain enzymes produced by bacteria

contain enzymes that can work at low temperatures (*e.g. 40°C*) which

- saves on heating water
- is better for clothes damaged by high temperature

Stains in clothing caused by proteins and fats are digested by the enzymes allowing easy removal

ANTIBIOTICS

are chemicals (*e.g. penicillin*) which prevent the growth of microbes (*e.g. bacteria*)

A range of antibiotics are needed to treat bacterial diseases because

- each one is only effective against certain bacteria

- patients may be allergic to a particular antibiotic

- bacteria can become **resistant** to a particular antibiotic

IMMOBILISATION

is when enzymes or cells are deliberately attached to a substance to hold them in place (*e.g. yeast in gel, enzyme onto glass beads*)

allows **continuous flow** processing

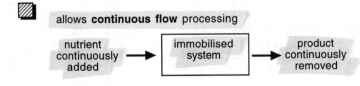

nutrient continuously added → immobilised system → product continuously removed

Advantages of continuous flow over batch processing are

- products are easily separated

- no time wasted in setting up another system

- there is less waste

FOOD TESTS

Food Type	Test	Colour	
		before	after
starch	add iodine solution	brown	blue-black
simple sugar	add Benedict's solution and heat to boiling	blue	orange/red

APPENDIX 2 PROBLEM SOLVING

he elements marked ✳ are dealt with in detail on the following pages

andling and processing information

You must be able to

select information from:-
texts
tables
pie charts
keys
graphs ✳
diagrams

present information in the form of:- summaries
tables
graphs ✳
pie charts ✳
histograms
keys ✳

do calculations to find:- percentages ✳
averages ✳
ratios ✳

comment on experimental design with regard to:-
validity ✳
improvements ✳
limitations ✳
error ✳

GRAPHS - reading graphs

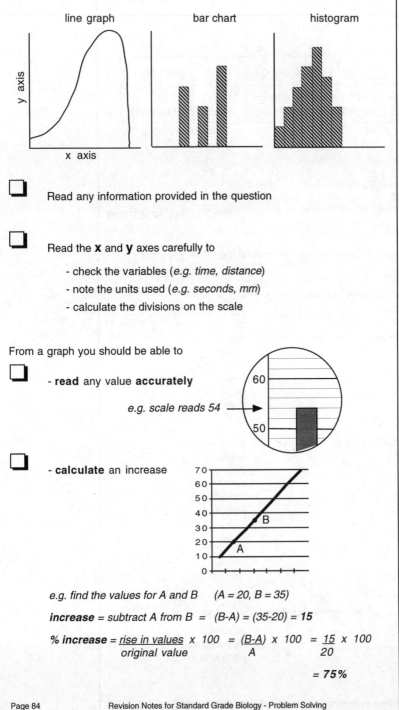

line graph   bar chart   histogram

y axis

x axis

☐ Read any information provided in the question

☐ Read the **x** and **y** axes carefully to

- check the variables (*e.g. time, distance*)
- note the units used (*e.g. seconds, mm*)
- calculate the divisions on the scale

From a graph you should be able to

☐ - **read** any value **accurately**

e.g. scale reads 54 ➔

60

50

☐ - **calculate** an increase

70
60
50
40
30   B
20
10   A
0

e.g. find the values for A and B   *(A = 20, B = 35)*

increase = *subtract A from B* = *(B-A)* = *(35-20)* = **15**

% increase = $\frac{rise\ in\ values}{original\ value}$ × *100* = $\frac{(B-A)}{A}$ × *100* = $\frac{15}{20}$ × *100*

= **75%**

- **calculate** a decrease

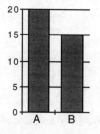

e.g. find the values for A and B   (A = 20, B = 15)

decrease = subtract B from A = (A-B) = (20-15) = **5**

% decrease = fall in values x 100 = (A-B) x 100 = 5 x 100
               original value   A   20

                                                    = **25%**

- **add up** a total

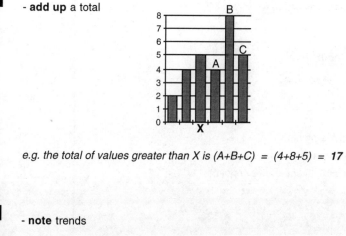

e.g. the total of values greater than X is (A+B+C) = (4+8+5) = **17**

- **note** trends

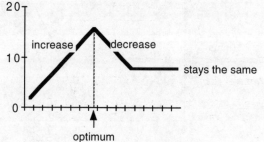

GRAPHS - drawing graphs (from a set of results)

☐ Decide on which type of graph (line, bar or histogram) you have to draw

☐ Decide which variable is to be plotted on each axis
Looking at the figures may give you a clue
i.e.   *x axis - values usually rise in regular intervals*
      y axis - experimental results, usually irregular

☐ Select a suitable scale
- rising in **regular** steps (not necessarily starting at 0)
- spread out to occupy most of the axis

☐ Label the axes clearly
- name of variable (*e.g. time*)
- unit used (*e.g. minutes*)

☐ Plot the values **accurately**

☐ **line graph**
- join up the points
- only between the values plotted
- use a straight line between points

e.g. results

pH	Time (mins)
4	24
5	10
6	2
7	1
8	4
9	18
10	28

e.g. line graph

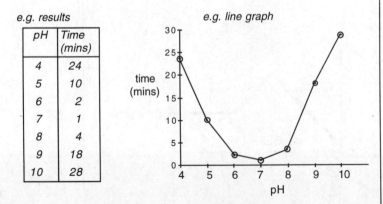

bar chart

- draw bars of the same width
- shade to distinguish if necessary

e.g. results

e.g. bar graph

Tongue rolling in a
group of children

	boys	girls
rollers	25	22
non-rollers	14	10

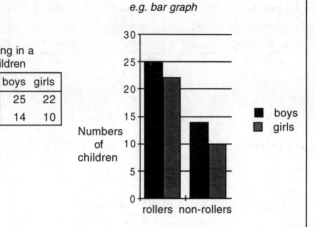

pie charts

- typical values as   percentages
segments of a clockface

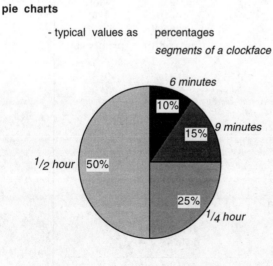

KEYS

You may be asked to complete a key from some information

e.g.

Plant	Leaf veins	Flower shape	Petals	Leaf shape
Bluebell	parallel	bell	regular	narrow
Daffodil	parallel	trumpet	regular	narrow
Deadnettle	branched	trumpet	irregular	broad
Celandine	branched	flat	regular	heart
Primrose	branched	trumpet	regular	oval

There are two major types of key

☐ **branched key** (or family tree key)

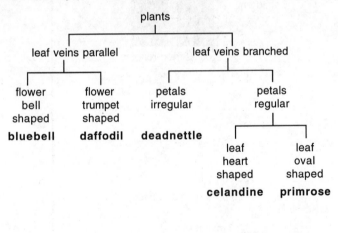

☐ **paired statement key**

1	leaf veins parallel	go to 2
	leaf veins branched	go to 3
2	flower bell-shaped	**bluebell**
	flower trumpet-shaped	**daffodil**
3	petals irregular	**deadnettle**
	petals regular	go to 4
4	leaf heart-shaped	**celandine**
	leaf oval-shaped	**primrose**

Revision Notes for Standard Grade Biology - Problem Solving

CALCULATIONS

❑

percentages

e.g. number of seeds planted 250

number of seeds germinated 150

% germination rate = $\dfrac{number}{original}$ x 100 = $\dfrac{150}{250}$ x 100 = **60%**

❑

averages

e.g.

Seed	Weight (g)
A	8
B	7
C	4
D	3
E	7
F	7

add up total of all the values 36

divide by the number of values 6

average weight = $\dfrac{36}{6}$ g = **6 g**

❑

ratios

e.g. number of purple seeds 21, number of yellow seeds 7

ratio of purple seeds to yellow seeds = 21 : 7

ratio = *(divide both by the lowest number)* = $\dfrac{21}{7} : \dfrac{7}{7}$ = **3 : 1**

EXPERIMENTAL DESIGN

❑

Making experiments fair

- only one variable
- all other factors constant
- set up a **control** (which is **identical** to the experimental set up but differs by **one** important factor)

❑

Making experiments reliable

- take many readings
- repeat the experiment
- pool results